Lucas Piano Room

LucasPianoRoom

Anime Piano, Compendium Five

1st edition 2023

Cover design: LucasPianoRoom
Music notation: LucasPianoRoom
Layout: LucasPianoRoom

Made in Germany

www.lucaspianoroom.com

Contents

Juyuu no Tsubasa

From "Attack on Titan"

Linked Horizon

Shinzo wa Sasageyo

From "Attack on Titan"

Linked Horizon

Resolution

From "Boruto: Naruto Next Generations"

Yasuharu Taklanshi

Spring Wind

From "Clannad"

Shinji Orito

7

Nezuko's Theme (Soft Ver.)

From "Demon Slayer"

Go Shiina

Conan's Theme (Ballad Version)

From "Detective Conan"

Katsuo Ono

Sentimental Ayumi

From "Detective Conan"

Katsuo Ono

We Gotta Power

From "Dragon Ball Z"

Keiju Ishikawa

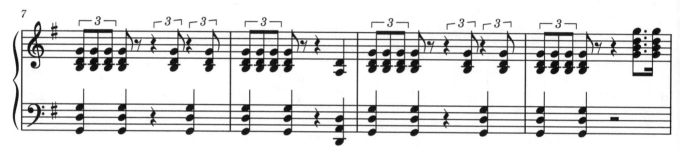

Tears in the Past

From "Erased"

Yuki Kajiura

Ancient Magic

From "Fairy Tail"

Yasuharu Takanashi

Charle no Kokuhaku

From "Fairy Tail"

Yasuharu Takanashi

Main Theme

From "Fairy Tail"

Yasuharu Takanashi

Grief

From "Fate/Zero"

Yuki Kajiura

Painful

From "Fate/Zero"

Yuki Kajiura

Ingenium

From "My Hero Academia"

Yuki Hayashi

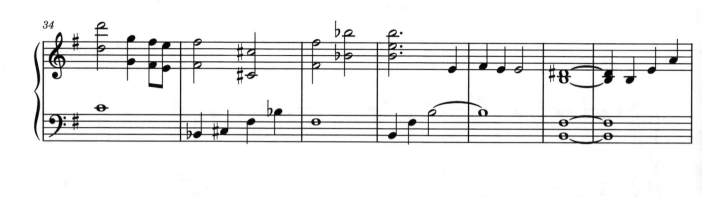

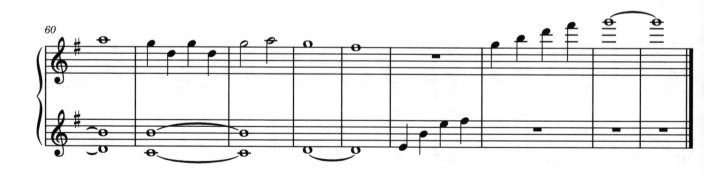

Resting Symbol of Peace

From "My Hero Academia"

Yuki Hayashi

Orochimaru's Theme

From "Naruto"

Toshio Masuda

Nagareboshi

From "Naruto Shippuden"

Yasuharu Takanashi

Obito's Theme

From "Naruto Shippuden"

Yasuharu Takanashi

Pain's Theme

From "Naruto Shippuden"

Yasuharu Takanashi

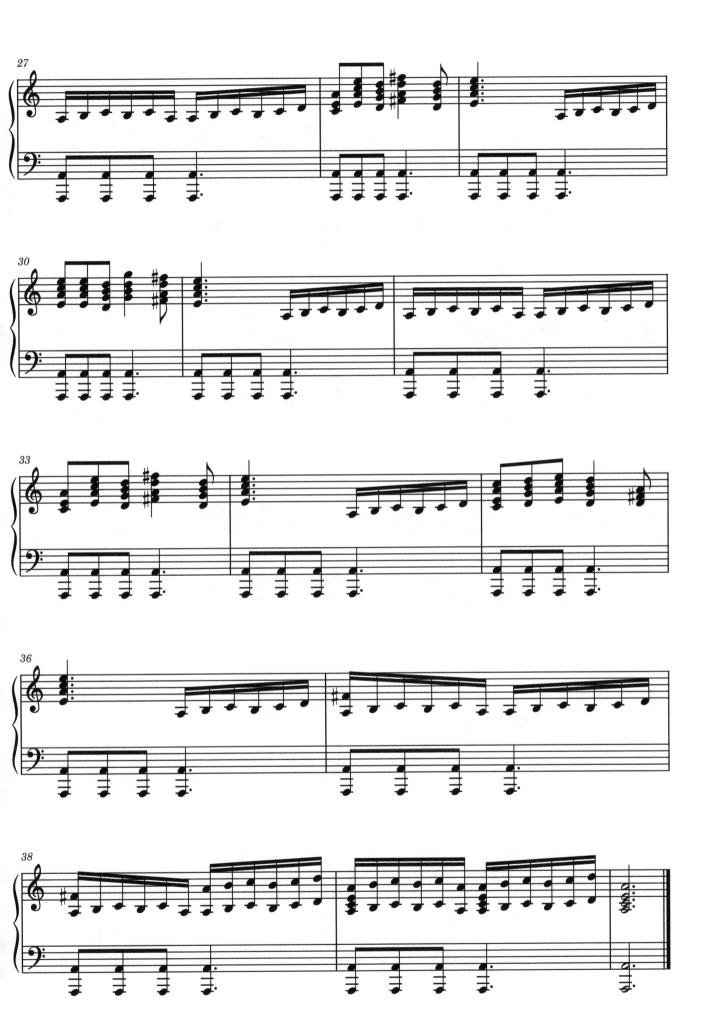

Setting Sun

From "Naruto Shippuden"

Yasuharu Takanashi

Akkisu's Music Box

From "One Piece"

Kohei Tanaka

Die Legende

From "One Piece"

Andy Knote

Next To You

From "Parasyte"

Ken Arai

Good Bye, Again and Again

From "Sword Art Online"

Yuki Kajiura

She Is Still Sleeping

From "Sword Art Online"

Yuki Kajiura

Think Tenderly of You

From "Sword Art Online"

Yuki Kajiura

You Are Not Alone (Soft Ver.)

From "Sword Art Online"

Yuki Kajiura

Walt

From "Terror in Resonance"

Yoko Kanno

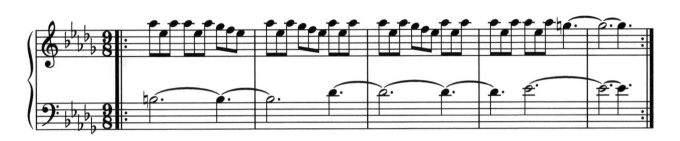

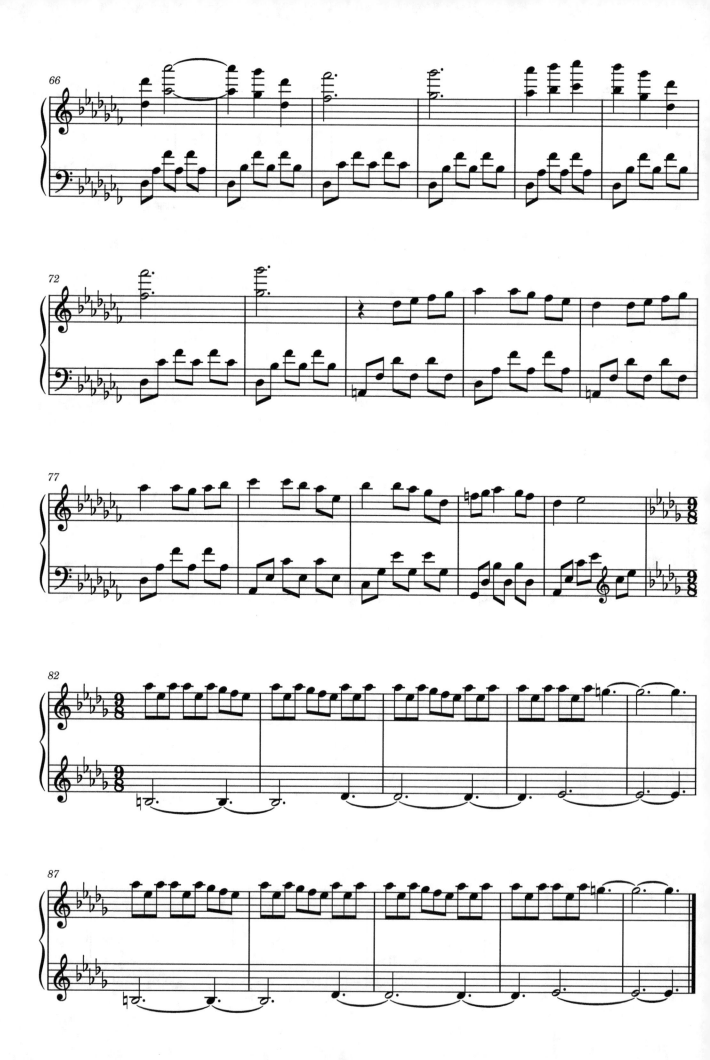

72-:THE1/KG-GR-4

From "The Seven Deadly Sins"

Hiroyuki Sawano

104EYES-Piano2

From "The Seven Deadly Sins"

Hiroyuki Sawano

104EYES-Piano3

From "The Seven Deadly Sins

Hiroyuki Sawano

104EYES-Piano4

From "The Seven Deadly Sins"

Hiroyuki Sawano

Rize's Melody

From "Tokyo Ghoul"

Yutaka Yamada

Memories

From "Tokyo Ghoul:re"

Yutaka Yamada

Reflections

From "Tokyo Ghoul:re"

Yutaka Yamada

Michishirube

From "Violet Evergarden"

Daisuke Kikuta

Hoshi wa Yoru Kagayakunda ze

From "Your Lie in April"

Masaru Yokoyama

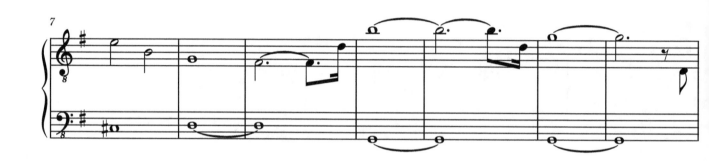

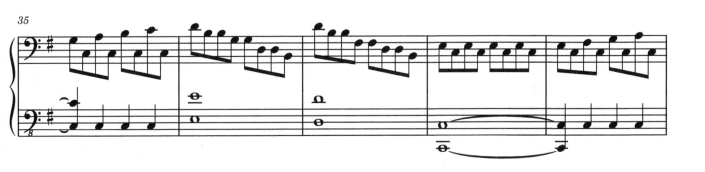

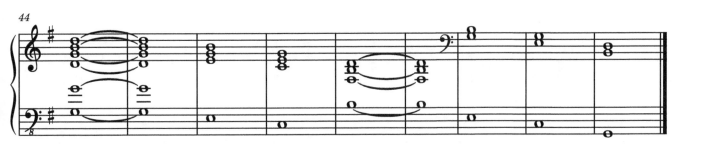

Kouiu Kimochi wo Nante Itta kana

From "Your Lie in April"

Masaru Yokoyama

Uso to Honto

From "Your Lie in April"

Masaru Yokoyama

Thank you for buying this product!

With this book you have 40 beautiful piano pieces from the most popular anime.

But that's not all!

Find many more anime piano pieces on my website, let a lot of tutorials on YouTube help you to learn all my pieces or just relax a bit while you listen to my music on Spotify & Apple Music.

Don't forget to visit me, but more importantly I hope you...

...have fun with this book!

Visit me on
www.lucaspianoroom.com

Search LucasPianoRoom on
YouTube

Search LucasPianoRoom on
Spotify & Apple Music

Printed in the USA
CPSIA information can be obtained
at www.ICGtesting.com
LVHW071449171223
766686LV00022B/1663